CATATONIA
INTERNATIONAL VELVET

SONY/ATV MUSIC PUBLISHING

EXCLUSIVE DISTRIBUTORS:
MUSIC SALES LIMITED
8/9 FRITH STREET, LONDON W1V 5TZ, ENGLAND.
MUSIC SALES PTY LIMITED
120 ROTHSCHILD AVENUE, ROSEBERY,
NSW 2018, AUSTRALIA.

ORDER NO.AM953854
ISBN 0-7119-7190-0

THIS BOOK © COPYRIGHT 1998 BY
SONY/ATV MUSIC PUBLISHING.

VISIT THE INTERNET MUSIC SHOP AT
http://www.musicsales.co.uk

MUSIC ARRANGED BY DEREK JONES.
(EXCEPT MULDER AND SCULLY - ARRANGED BY ROGER DAY).
MUSIC PROCESSED BY PAUL EWERS MUSIC DESIGN.

PRINTED IN THE UNITED KINGDOM BY
CALIGRAVING LIMITED, THETFORD, NORFOLK.

YOUR GUARANTEE OF QUALITY:
AS PUBLISHERS, WE STRIVE TO PRODUCE EVERY
BOOK TO THE HIGHEST COMMERCIAL STANDARDS.

THE MUSIC HAS BEEN FRESHLY ENGRAVED AND,
WHILST ENDEAVOURING TO RETAIN THE ORIGINAL
RUNNING ORDER OF THE RECORDED ALBUM,
THE BOOK HAS BEEN CAREFULLY DESIGNED TO
MINIMISE AWKWARD PAGE TURNS AND TO MAKE
PLAYING FROM IT A REAL PLEASURE.

PARTICULAR CARE HAS BEEN GIVEN TO
SPECIFYING ACID-FREE, NEUTRAL-SIZED
PAPER MADE FROM PULPS WHICH HAVE NOT BEEN
ELEMENTAL CHLORINE BLEACHED.

THIS PULP IS FROM FARMED SUSTAINABLE
FORESTS AND WAS PRODUCED WITH SPECIAL
REGARD FOR THE ENVIRONMENT.

THROUGHOUT, THE PRINTING AND BINDING
HAVE BEEN PLANNED TO ENSURE A STURDY,
ATTRACTIVE PUBLICATION WHICH SHOULD GIVE
YEARS OF ENJOYMENT.

IF YOUR COPY FAILS TO MEET OUR HIGH STANDARDS,
PLEASE INFORM US AND WE WILL GLADLY REPLACE IT.

MUSIC SALES' COMPLETE CATALOGUE
DESCRIBES THOUSANDS OF TITLES AND IS
AVAILABLE IN FULL COLOUR SECTIONS BY SUBJECT,
DIRECT FROM MUSIC SALES LIMITED.
PLEASE STATE YOUR AREAS OF INTEREST
AND SEND A CHEQUE/POSTAL ORDER FOR £1.50
FOR POSTAGE TO: MUSIC SALES LIMITED,
NEWMARKET ROAD, BURY ST. EDMUNDS,
SUFFOLK IP33 3YB.

MULDER AND SCULLY

WORDS & MUSIC BY MATTHEWS/ROBERTS/CATATONIA

1. I'd ra-ther be li-be-ra-ted,
(Verse 2 see block lyric)

I find my-self cap-ti-va-ted, stop

do-ing what you keep do-ing it too.

you, is there no-thing I can do, must we all march in

two by two, by_____ two.

D.%. al Coda

⊕ *Coda*

-lone here._____ Things are get-ting strange, I'm

start-ing to wor - ry, this could be a case for Mul- der and Scul - ly.

things are get-ting strange now I can't sleep a - lone.

So what have you got to say a-bout that, and what does some-one
do with-out love, and what does some-one
do with love, and what have you got to

Play 3 times

Repeat ad lib. to fade

say a - bout that?

Verse 2:
I'd rather be jumping ship
I find myself jumping straight in
Stop doing what you
Keep doing it too.

Forever be dozy and dim
I wake myself thinking of him
Stop doing what you
Keep doing it too.

Verse 3:
And as for some happy ending
I'd rather stay single and thin
Stop doing what you
Keep doing it to me.

GAME ON

WORDS & MUSIC BY MATTHEWS/ROBERTS/CATATONIA

1. You know the time to act is now.
(Verses 2 & 3 see block lyrics)

Do do do do. Be-fore the sands of time run out.

Do do do do. I know___ that I___ could nev - er

fall from grace, I'm far___ too clev - er.   ___ too clev - er. Do do

do do.___ Na___ na___ na.___

Na___ na___ na___ na.___ Na___ na___

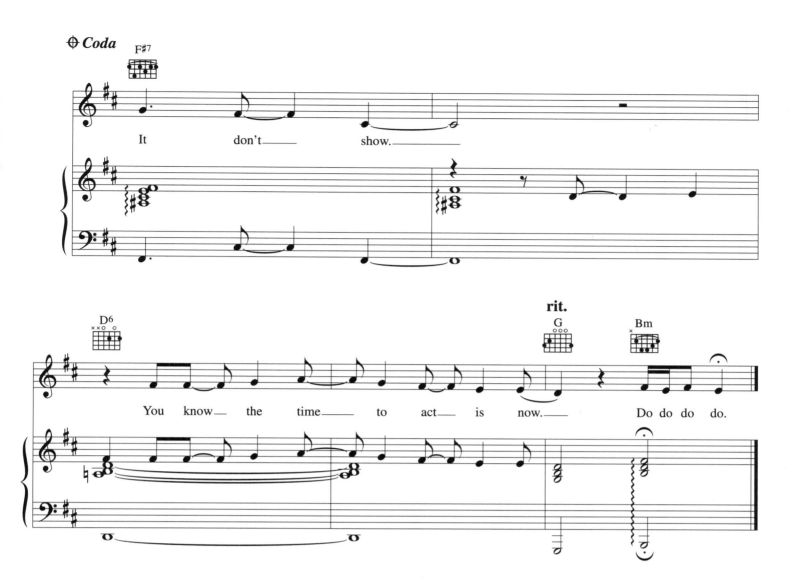

Verse 2:
I will achieve my destiny.
Do do do do.
My star's ascent a certainty.
Do do do do.
I know that I could never
Fall from grace, I'm far too clever.

Verse 3 (𝄋):
No clever clevers can dissuade.
Do do do do.
From tougher substance I was made.
Do do do do.
I know that I could never
Fall from grace, I'm far too clever.

I AM THE MOB

WORDS & MUSIC BY ROBERTS/CATATONIA

Lu - ca Bra - si ah, he sleeps____ with the fish - es. Lu - ca Bra - si ah, he sleeps

____ with the fish - es mis - sus.

ROAD RAGE

WORDS & MUSIC BY MATTHEWS/ROBERTS/CATATONIA

best days.

Space age, road rage, fast lane. And if all —

— you've — got to do —— to - day — is find — peace of mind —

come here, — you — can take a piece — of mine. —

You could be tak-ing it ea - sy on — your - self. You should be mak-ing it ea-

JOHNNY COME LATELY

WORDS & MUSIC BY CATATONIA

know that_____ you would hate me._____ If I'd told you that I made some time and

stayed be - hind to find out how to make a gar - den_____ grow._____

_____ Where the sun no long - er shines._____

_____ He as - sured me that the seeds you sold were sound but I must have cast them all on_____

ston - y ground. And now the

sun won't shine. I must have

asked too ma - ny ques - tions and stayed be - hind to find out how to make a

gar - den grow. But he nev - er ev - er gave a - way the

se - cret of this god - for - sa - ken_____ soil._____

Verse 2:
If I envied the things that he spoke of
How I envied the things that he thought of
He was a Johnny Come Lately
And I know that you would hate me.

Verse 3 (%):
He didn't need us, just tempted and teased us
You could've been here, wishing you were here
This was a Johnny Come Lately
And I know that you would hate me.

GOLDFISH AND PARACETAMOL

WORDS & MUSIC BY MATTHEWS/JONES/CATATONIA

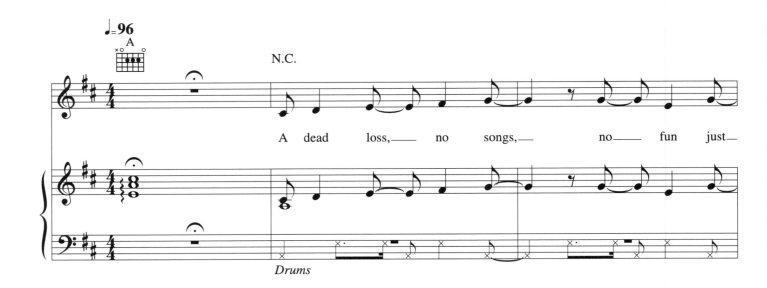

A dead loss, no songs, no fun just

glum. Ly-ing next to some-one. So don't men-tion the War,

(Verse 3 see block lyric)

Drums cont.

don't ques-tion where we stand, nor where we fall.

1. North, South, East where's best? If I head left it turns out di-
(Verse 2 see block lyric)

-rec-tion-less. And nee-dle point a-side, I al-ways find

em-broid-er-y leaves me blind. 'Cos I'm too wea-ry to rest since I no-ticed

com-ing se-cond best is close to i-deal.

Verse 2:
What fools boredom breeds
So much to do
So many goldfish to feed
And paracetamol
I take them all
They line my stomach wall.

'Cos I'm too weary *etc.*

Verse 3 (%):
With customary thirst
I search a water glass
But gin hits first
Oh don't believe the hype
Expectancy will always spoil a party.
It's tourniquet by crochet
My waters break
Don't drive for pity's sake.

'Cos I'm too weary *etc.*

INTERNATIONAL VELVET

WORDS & MUSIC BY ROBERTS/CATATONIA

De - ffrwch Cym - ry - cys - glyd gwlad y gân

To Coda ⊕

dwfn   yw'r   gwen - did——

bych - an— yw   y   fflam.——

G7

1. Creu - lon   yw'r   cyn-hae - af   ond per——   yw'r   dôn.——
(Verse 2 see block lyric)

'Da'   al - aw'r   al - arch   un - ig   yn——   fy   mron.

Thank the Lord— I'm, thank the Lord— I'm

Welsh.

D.%. al Coda
Repeat 4 times ad lib.

Coda

Ev - er - y day_____ when I wake up_____ I

Verse 2:
Gwledd o fedd gynhyrfodd Cymraes swil
Darganfyddais gwir baradwys Rhyl.

Every day when I wake up *etc.*

WHY I CAN'T STAND ONE NIGHT STANDS

WORDS & MUSIC BY ROBERTS/CATATONIA

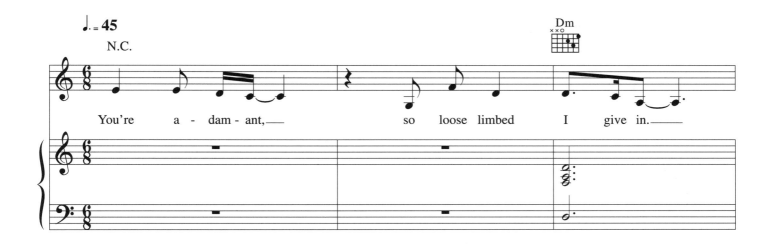

You're a-dam-ant,___ so loose limbed I give in.___

Al-though your bed___ is warm the worn springs

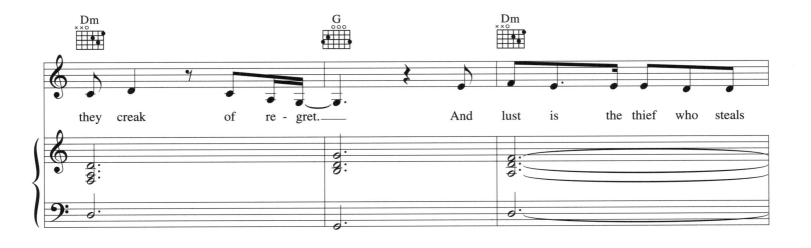

they creak of re-gret.___ And lust is the thief who steals

PART OF THE FURNITURE

WORDS & MUSIC BY MATTHEWS/CATATONIA

you're warm - - -er. Be your cra - dle,

swing you un - til you're tired out.

You say the words and I could be them, take your pick and I could be there.

stringendo

DON'T NEED THE SUNSHINE

WORDS & MUSIC BY POWELL/CATATONIA

1. Well it's a most pe-cu-li-ar feel-
(Verse 3 see block lyric)

-ing_____ like sun - burn in the eve - 'ning.   With

dark_____ clouds   on_____ their   way.

And   you   think   it's   most   un - like - ly_____   your   life   could

ev - er shine_ as bright - ly.   Once the sun has gone_ and the

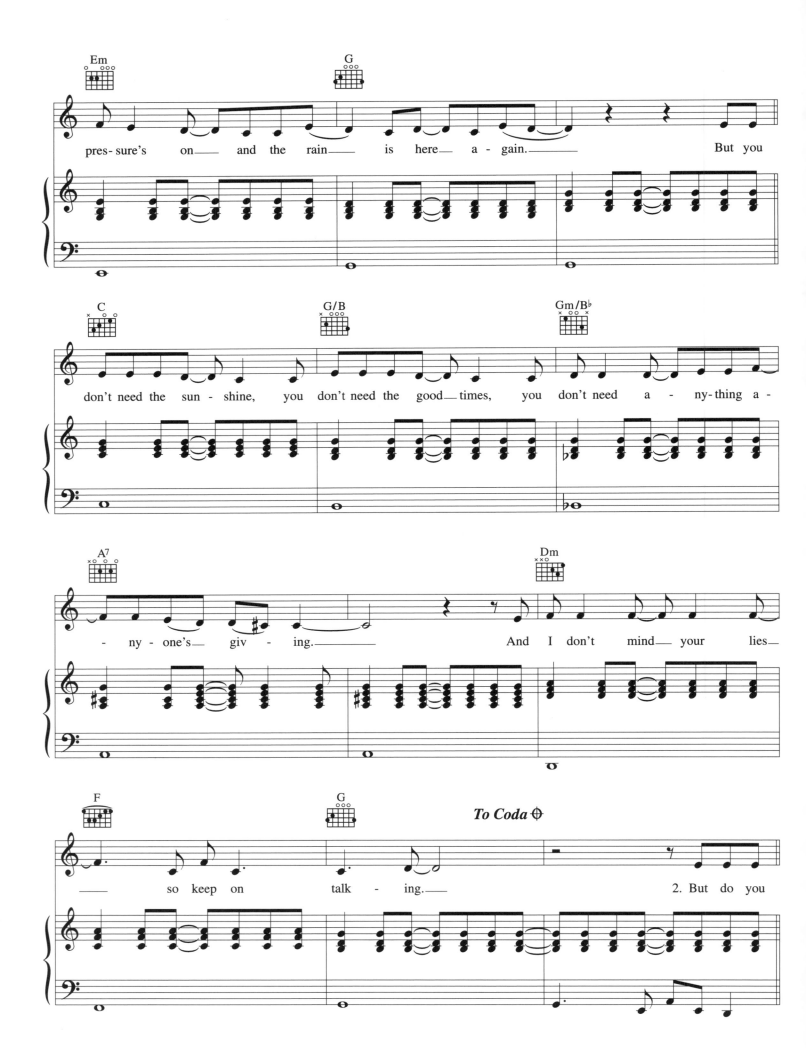

find the change— in the sea - sons———— af - fects you with-out rea-

- son? You've greet - ings— but no - thing more— to say.—

And you swear you'd feel much bet -

- ter——— if on - ly Sum-mer'd last— for - ev - er. But the

don't need the sun - shine, you don't need the good— times, don't need a - ny-thing a-

-ny - one's giv - ing._____ And I____ don't mind— your lies____

____ so keep on talk - ing.____ Well I

The Don't need the sun - shine,
rain has

Verse 3 (𝄎):
Well I throw away my sunshines
My so-called little lifelines
Do you know what I mean?
When I decided that the answer
Could not be bought across the counter
My sister dista has left for good
Now the rain has gone away.

And you don't need the sunshine *etc.*

STRANGE GLUE

WORDS & MUSIC BY POWELL / CATATONIA

Lyrics:
It was strange glue that held us to-geth-er while we both came a-part at the seams. She said

I clothe them and feed them. And I smile, yes I
(I'll)   (I'll)

smile as they're tak-ing me ov-er. And if I

can-not sleep for the se-crets I keep, it's the price I'm will-ing to

meet. The end of the night nev-er comes too quick-ly

for me.

D.%. al Coda

Oh._____ But I

⊕ *Coda*

And if I can-not sleep for the se-crets I keep, it's the

prize I'm wait-ing to steal. Oh the end___ of the night___ nev-er

comes too quick-ly for me.____ And I smile. The end____ of the night____ nev-er

comes too quick-ly for me.____ And I smile,____ smile, smile as they're

tak-ing me ov-er.____ And I smile._____ The end____ of the night____ nev-er

comes too quick-ly for me,____ nev-er comes too quick-ly for me.

MY SELFISH GENE

WORDS & MUSIC BY ROBERTS/CATATONIA

2. You, me and des-ti-ny,
(Verse 3 see block lyric)
I am court-ed by un-

-cer-tain-ty.
I've lost my will— to live— un-self-ish-ly.

Al-tru-i—sm stinks of— fal-la-cy.— And my self-fish gene it

fills my spleen with bile.———— And all——— the while I thought you gave a

Verse 3:
You, me and Destiny
Guess that it was never meant to be
All you needed was some courtesy
And I'm not waiting for apologies.

My selfish gene *etc.*